Collecting Hull Pottery's
Little Red Riding Hood
a pictorial reference and price guide

by
Mark and Ellen Supnick

Published by
L-W Book Sales
P.O. Box 69
Gas City, IN 46933

ISBN #: 0-9611446-1-0

Additional autographed copies may be purchased
from Mark & Ellen Supnick - 2771 Oakbrook Manor-
Ft. Lauderdale, FL 33332 - Phone# 954-389-3911
Website address: http://www.sunshinejars.com
email address: ellen@sunshinejars.com

Published by: L-W Book Sales
                PO Box 69
                Gas City, IN 46933

Please write for our free catalog

Printed in the U.S.A. by Image Graphics

Other books written by Mark and Ellen Supnick include
Collecting Shawnee Pottery,
The Wonderful World of Cookie Jars,
Published by L-W Book Sales

Table of Contents

Dedication 4

Acknowledgments 5

About Collecting Little Red Riding Hood 6

Introduction 7

Patent Information 7-8

Background Information 9

Marks 10

Letters That Answer Questions 11-12

Decals, Colors and Trim 13-16

Pricing Information 17

Advertising Plaque & Rare Items 18

Cookie Jars 19-29

Cracker Jars 30-32

Dresser Jars 33-34

Grease Jars 35

Sugar and Creamers 36-38

Baby Dishes 39, 64

Batter Pitcher 40

Milk Pitcher 41-42

Casserole Dish 43, 73

Cannisters 44-53

Spice Jars 54-58

Standing Bank 59

Wall Hanging Bank 60, 72

Standing Planter 61

Wall Hanging Planter 62

Teapots 63

Mugs 64-65

Salt and Peppers 66-67

Lamp 68

Match Boxes 69-70

Mustard Jar 71

Stringholder 72

Price Guide 74-77

Dedication

*This book is dedicated to the late Pearl Supnick.
She started us on this wonderful journey,
we just want to say "Thanks".*

Acknowledgments

It seems that to research, produce, catalog, list, price, photograph, and publish a guide of this type is nothing less than an impossible task without the help of so many people. I only hope that I don't leave anyone out. My gratitude can never be truly expressed.

Glenn Smith deserves a special acknowledgment for all the help he has given me regarding the photography of key items in his collection. He not only gave his permission to photograph these items for this book, but due to the high risk probability of shipping he carried the items to his local photographer and sent me the required transparencies. His help, in so many ways, is greatly appreciated.

A special thank you goes out to Steve Johnson and Wayne Bolin for all of their contributions made to this book.

Ginny Hall whose love for "Little Red Riding Hood" has only been exceeded by her persistence in research. She shared all and gave all. It was refreshing to meet someone so giving.

Heartfelt thanks go the the following people: Brenda Roberts, author of *"The Collectors Encyclopedia of Hull Pottery"*. Jo Ann Schliesmann for allowing me to reproduce a photograph from *"Price Survey 3rd Edition"* written by her late husband Mark Schliesmann. Trish Claar for her help in obtaining patent copies and related information. Joan Hull for her continuous support and vast knowledge of Hull Pottery. Sharon Huxford co-author of *"Collectors Encyclopedia of Art Pottery"* for her support and advise.

Of course to Louise Elizabeth Bauer, the designer of patent #135,889 and her many other beautiful creations.

Also, Neil Wood for being so wonderful and supportive.

About Collecting Little Red Riding Hood
What you need to know

It is now 1998 and the search for the beautiful Little Red Riding Hood is hotter than ever before.

One of the important pointers I tell all of my customers is that Regal China produced most of all the Little Red Riding Hood pieces and they were made from Vitrified China. Hull Pottery that made some the 967 Hull Ware cookie jars used a cream colored pottery distinctively different in look, feel and color.

This was never a problem in the past everyone knew when they bought a piece of Little Red Riding Hood they were buying the real thing. However, today it is a different world in Antiquing and Collecting pottery, you have to be educated in what you collect.

It pains us to see people spending so much money buying Red Riding Hood pieces when they are actually buying reproductions. This is so unfortunate. The only way to stop this is to study the pottery and buy Red Riding Hood from legitimate dealers. I stress dealers over anyone else. So many Antique shops are now carrying these reproductions and they are not marked appropriately. I am not saying that all Antique Shops are out to get you, most of these shops have many different dealers in them that have displays of many different items. There is no way they can police all these people. You can ask for a money back guarantee from the shop owner before leaving, that they will guarantee the authenticity of the pottery, and you want a money back guarantee.

I receive so many calls every week from people who were "had" by people in flea markets and elsewhere. I stress to all of you please, please be careful when buying. This is a wonderful collectible that has grown in value over the years and it will continue to grow, just be careful buying and watch who you are buying from. Enjoy collecting this wonderful precious Little Red Riding Hood pottery, you are buying true treasures from the past.

Ellen Supnick

Introduction

A.E. Hull Company was formed in July of 1905. It continued until 1986 and at that time discontinued all operations.

A.E. Hull Sr. remained at control of the company until his death in 1930. For the next seven years his son A.E. Hull Jr. carried out a strong management program that allowed the company to survive through the "Great Depression". He resigned in March of 1937 to become President and Chief Executive Officer of the "Shawnee Pottery Company". He remained with Shawnee until March 21, 1950. Later becoming President of the "Western Stoneware Company". Gerald F. Watts succeeded A.E. Hull Jr. as President in 1937. Through his control he led the company through many changes until January 1952. At that time the company changed its name to "The Hull Pottery Company" and J.B. Hull succeeded Gerald F. Watts as President. In 1978 the death of J.B. Hull changed the structure of the company and Henry Sulens became President.

It was during the years of Gerald F. Watts presidency that Hull introduced "Hull Ware" Little Red Riding Hood, and so it began.

"Little Red Riding Hood"
Patent Design 135,889
June 29, 1943
Louise Elizabeth Bauer

Produced and Distributed
1943 to 1957

Patent Information

Patented June 29, 1943

Des. 135,889

UNITED STATES PATENT OFFICE

135,889

DESIGN FOR A COOKIE JAR

Louise Elizabeth Bauer, Zanesville, Ohio, assignor to The A. E. Hull Pottery Company, Incorporated, Crooksville, Ohio, a corporation of Ohio

Application April 12, 1943, Serial No. 109,959

Term of patent 7 years

To all whom it may concern:

Be it known that I, Louise Elizabeth Bauer, a citizen of the United States, residing at Zanesville, in the county of Muskingum and State of Ohio, have invented a new, original, and ornamental Design for a Cookie Jar, of which the following is a specification, reference being had to the accompanying drawing, forming part thereof.

Figure 1 is a front elevational view of a cookie jar showing my new design, and

Figure 2 is a side elevational view thereof.

I claim:

The ornamental design for a cookie jar, as shown.

LOUISE ELIZABETH BAUER.

Please note that Louise Elizabeth Bauer assigned her rights to patent design #135,889 to "The A.E. Hull Pottery Company" Incorporated, Crooksville, Ohio, a corporation of Ohio.

Patent Information

June 29, 1943.   L. E. BAUER   Des. 135,889

COOKIE JAR

Filed April 12, 1943

Fig. 1.   *Fig. 2.*

Inventor

LOUISE E. BAUER

By   Clarence A. O'Brien
and Harvey B. Jackson
Attorneys

8

Background Information

With the assignment of patent #135,889 the A.E. Hull Company started production of "Little Red Riding Hood" and it soon developed a great demand. The A.E. Hull Company did not trim or decorate any of the items. The blank undecorated items were sent to Royal China and Novelty Company of Chicago, Illinois who in turn did all the gold, paint, and decal work required. They were then returned to A.E. hull for distribution. Pure white blanks are found today in almost all of the models but demand calls for prices between 25% to 50% lower then that of the finished decorated models.

It is the belief of this author that A.E. Hull Company only produced some of the early cookie jars, marked "#967 Hull Ware, Little Red Riding Hood, Patent Applied for USA" and the dresser jar with large bow in front marked "Hull Ware#932 USA". These items are the only ones that have the typical creamy off white pottery consistent with Hull's other lines.

Items other than the two described above all have a bright white china that is inconsistent with the other lines of the A.E. Hull Company. This bright white china along with the paint, decorations, and type of design is consistent with the type of items that were produced by "The Royal China and Novelty Company" a division of the "Regal China Corporation." The Regal China Corporation did produce a kitchen novelty line called "Old McDonalds Farm". This line of kitchen novelty items follows very closely that of "Little Red Riding Hood". They both have canister sets, spice sets, salt and pepper sets, teapots, covered sugars, creamers, grease jars, and both carry a patent design number on the underside of many items.

In a letter to a collector Louise Bauer states that "These models were made for Royal China and Novelty Company of Chicago, Illinois". Her patents clearly assign the rights to patent 135,889 to the A.E. Hull Company. It is my assumption that "Royal China and Novelty Company" and or "Regal China Corporation" did, in fact, produce the vast majority of what we call "Hull's Little Red Riding Hood" under contract to the A.H. Hull Company.

Marks

There are five basic types of markings that are found on "Little Red Riding Hood".

1. Written in script.
   Mid-1940's
   Found on Cookie Jar

   967
   Hull Ware
   Little Red Riding Hood
   Patent Applied for
   USA

2. Written in script
   Mid-1940's

   Hull Ware
   U.S.A.

3. Written in script
   and block letters
   Found on Cookie Jar

   Little Red Riding Hood
   Pat-Des-No-135889
   U.S.A.

4. Written in block letters
   Late 1940's to Mid-1950's

   Pat-Des-No-135889
   U.S.A.

5. Block

   Pat. 135889
   or 135889

There are many items that are not marked at all. Most collectors, after seeing four or five marked items, can easily identify this wonderful line.

Many items shown in this guide as marked or unmarked may be found either way.

Letters That Answer Questions

Sometimes there are no answers, sometimes we can assume, and then sometimes we get help. Below and on the next page are excerpts from two letters between a persistent collector and Louise Bauer.

"Dear Ms. _____   March 8, 1976

Thank you for your interest in the "Little Red Riding Hood" pattern.

In answer to your first question the only pieces which I designed were the cookie jar, a small table salt and pepper and a larger range size salt and pepper. These models were made for "Royal China and Novelty Company" of Chicago, Illinois.

To answer your second question - No I never designed another "Red Riding Hood" line under "Hull Art Ware".

It was so kind of you to write and I hope this answers your questions.

Sincerely
Louise Bauer

P.S. "When they took these items off the market I do not know".

Letters That Answer Questions

An answer to a questionnaire dated August 17, 1976 from Louise Bauer.

QUESTIONNAIRE
"Little Red Riding Hood"
Pat. Des. No. 135889

1. DID ROYAL CHINA PRODUCE ALL OF THESE RED RIDING HOOD PIECES UNDER YOUR PATTERN DESIGN NUMBER?

~ Except for those made at Hull Pottery Company, I believe Royal China produced the rest.

2. IF THEY DIDN'T, WHAT COMPANY BOUGHT THE RIGHTS TO IT AND PRODUCED IT?

~ As far as I know, no other company bought the rights to it.

3. SOME OF THE SO-CALLED "AUTHORITIES" CLAIM THAT HULL MADE BLANKS AND SENT THEM TO THE ROYAL CHINA & NOVELTY COMPANY TO BE DECORATED. IS THIS A FACT?

~ Yes they manufactured some but not all of them.

4. COULD YOU TELL ME THE APPROXIMATE YEAR THAT "LITTLE RED RIDING HOOD" CAME OUT ON THE MARKET?

~ It was started in production at the time the patent was registered.

5. DO YOU KNOW "WHAT" AND "HOW MANY" PIECES WERE PRODUCED UNDER THIS PAT. DES. NO. 135889?

~ Sorry but I don't know the answer to this one.

I was so interested to learn that so many pieces were made under this design patent. I wonder who copied it. Thanks so much for writing and I'm sorry Royal China didn't help you.

Sincerely
Louise Bauer

Decals, Colors, and Trim

There are many variations of gold trim, color trim, and three basic types of decals. These photos will help you identify the designs.

Poppy Flower Bouquet

This **Open End Cookie Jar** has the most basic and popular design that is found on most all models of the Little Red Riding Hood.

Decals, Colors, and Trim

Flower Sprig

This **Pretzel Canister** shows the flower sprig design found on many but not all models of the Little Red Riding Hood.

Decals, Colors, and Trim

Poinsettia Flower

This **Round Basket Cookie Jar with No Apron** *shows the poinsettia flower* *design. This design is rarely found on anything other than the "Green Basket* *Cookie Jar."*

Decals, Colors, and Trim

Decals were always placed on by hand before firing. Note below that the decals did not always lay out the same way.

Pictured here are **Three Standing Banks** *with the poppy decals all in different positions. The paint variations appear on many items. On the wolf jar, for example, both the bases and the wolves themselves are found in either red, yellow, black, and brown. See page 35.*

Some creamers and sugars have been seen in brown and yellow combinations as well as the standard colors of red, blue, yellow, brown, and gold.

Pricing

The initial price guide enclosed, was put together by means of questionnaires to collectors, prices listed in ads, values seen at shows and shops, and just general discussion with collectors and dealers alike throughout the country. This guide reflects the authors compilation of the above.

This price guide, as with most price guides, was designed to assist both the collector and the dealer. The prices quoted are to be used as a guide only, and were not intended to set prices.

The author assumes no responsibility for any losses that may occur as a result of consulting this guide.

When one compiles a price guide, there are always collectors and dealers who say the prices are too high or those who feel the prices are too low. Prices do vary from state to state and from time to time.

To sum up let me quote a highly respected collector who wrote me regarding his recent ad in *The Antique Trader.*
> "In my ad in the Antique Trader just recently, I asked $2,000
> for the baby dish, got the price, and wished I had eight more
> because I got that many calls from different collectors or dealers
> wanting to buy it."

Advertising Plaque & Other Rare Items

The **Framed Advertising Plaque** pictured in the back row of this photo was displayed by retailing dealers and today is extremely rare. It measures 6 1/2" high x 12" long and 3/8" thick.

The other pieces in this photo are from front row left to right: baby dish, covered casserole, mug, and another baby dish. The back row left to right: string holder, advertising plaque, and a wall bank.

All of these items are a great find! They are very rare and sought after.

Cookie Jar

This **Round Basket Cookie Jar with no Apron** has the poinsettia decals and is shown here with the matching **Medium Salt & Pepper Set.** The cookie jar measures 13" tall.

Cookie Jar

The **Open End Basket Cookie Jar with Apron** has an unusual orange and yellow floral design and measures 13″ tall.

Cookie Jar

This **Open End Basket Cookie Jar with Apron** has the brown rose decal and measures 13″ tall.

Cookie Jar

This **Open End Basket Cookie Jar with Apron** has the pink and grey floral pattern and measures 13″ tall. This jar is very rare.

Cookie Jar

This **Open End Basket Cookie Jar with Apron** has the closed poppy decal and measures 13″ tall.

Cookie Jar

This **Round Basket Cookie Jar with Apron** has the poppy floral string decal and measures 13″ tall.

Cookie Jar

This **Open End Basket Cookie Jar with Apron** has red trim on the base. This trim is very hard to find. Also note the foil label shown in this picture that reads "Hand Painted".

Cookie Jar

    This **Open End Basket Cookie Jar with Apron** has the most common decoration except you will notice the lid has extraordinary decorations and unusual green eyes. The jar measures 13" tall.

Cookie Jar

This photo shows a close-up of the unusual lid with the extra decoration and unusual green eyes shown on the previous page.

Cookie Jar

This **Round Basket Cookie Jar** with the poinsettia design is done in white and gold trim and measures 13" tall. This jar is considered very rare.

Cookie Jar

*Pictured are two **Open End Basket Cookie Jars** measuring 13" tall. The one on the left has the poppy bouquets design. The one on the right has the regular poppy decals but note the heavy paint decoration on the lid of this jar.*

Cracker Jar

This **Cracker Jar** *has the poppy decals and measures 8 1/4" tall.*

Cracker Jar

This all white **Cracker Jar** with gold trim measures 8 1/4″ tall, and is considered vary rare.

Cracker Jar

*These are seven variations of **Cracker Jars** with different decals.*

Dresser Jar

Pictured here with the dresser jar is the very rare doll head on the left that measures 4 1/4" tall. The middle piece is the dresser jar that measures 8 3/4" tall. On the right is a kneeling figurine measuring 5 1/4" tall.

Note: The doll head is a very early piece and notice how it matches the early kneeling figurine and the dresser jar.

Dresser Jar

These three **Dresser Jars** with different paint all measure 8 3/4" tall. The far left jar is cold painted, the middle jar is decorated underglaze and the jar on the right is pearlized underglaze.

Grease Jars

These three variations of **Grease Jars** all measure 6 1/2" tall, and all are unmarked. The one on the far left is a wolf jar in yellow, the middle one is red riding hood's basket, and the one on the right is a wolf jar in red.

It is important to note that there are two mold variations of the wolf, one has the ears up and the other has the ears down. The wolf jars are found in either red, yellow, black or brown. The wolf jar in reality was a grease jar.

Sugar and Creamer

Left item: **Tab Handled Creamer** *that measures 5" tall and has the poppy flower bouquet decals with no markings.*

Right item: **Crawling Creamer** *that measures 4" tall and is also unmarked, and has the poppy flower bouquet decals.*

Sugar and Creamer

Left item: **Covered Sugar** *that measures 4 1/2" tall
and has the poppy flower bouquet decals.*

Right item: **Ruffled-Skirt Creamer** *that measures 5" tall
and has the poppy flower bouquet decals.*

Sugar and Creamer Set

These matching pieces have the poppy floral string pattern decals.

Front Row Left to Right:
  Open Creamer, Small Salt and Pepper, and an Open Sugar.

Back Row:
  Round Basket Cookie Jar.

Baby Dishes

This **Baby Dish and Mug Set** is a rare find, and would truly be a welcome addition to any Red Riding Hood Collection, and it is marked with this pattern number:

Pat. Des. No. 135889

Batter Pitcher

This **Batter Pitcher** *measures 6 3/4″ tall and has the poppy decal design.*
Marked Pat. Des. No. 135889.

Milk Pitcher

This **Standing Milk Pitcher** with the poppy decal design measures 8" tall and is marked Pat. Des. No. 135889.

Milk Pitcher

The photo is reproduced from "Price Survey 3rd Edition" on page 109 by Mark Schliesmann, with the permission from Jo Ann Schliesmann.

*The **Ruffled Skirt Milk Pitcher** on the top row second item matches the **Pour Through the Head Creamer** on the bottom right, and is extremely rare.*

Casserole Dish

The **Casserole Dish with the red handle** is embossed with the Wolf, Little Red Riding Hood, Grandma, The Axman, and Grandma's House. It was then overglazed in a heavy Red Glaze reducing the clarity. For a closer look at the details, please see the baby dish shown on page 39.

This artist rendering is as close as I have ever been to this item. I have spoken to two people, including Brenda Roberts, author of "Collectors Encyclopedia of Hull Pottery", and have confirmed that it does exist.

The casserole measures 11 3/4" and is marked Pat. 135889.

Cannisters

The **Tidbits Cannister** *shown here is very rare and is marked Pat. Des. No. 135889.*

Cannisters

*Pictured here are two **Cannisters, a Cookies and a Popcorn**, both with poppy decals. Both cannisters are 9 1/2" tall.*

Cannisters

*A **Tea Cannisters** marked Pat. Des. No. 135889,*
with the floral poppy bouquet.

Cannisters

*A **Sugar Cannisters** marked Pat. Des. No. 135889,*
with the floral poppy bouquet.

Cannisters

*Pictured here are two **Cannisters, a Peanuts, and a Potato Chip,** both with poppy decals. These cannisters are considered very rare and are both 9 1/2" tall.*

A **Pretzel Cannister** *marked Pat. Des. No. 135889, with the floral poppy bouquet, this piece is considered rare.*

*A **Flour Cannister** marked Pat. Des. No. 135889, with the poppy decal.*

*A **Cereal Cannister** marked Pat. Des. No. 135889, with the spring flower decal. This piece is hard to find.*

*A **Coffee Cannister** marked Pat. Des. No. 135889, with the spring flower decal.*

*A **Salt Cannister**, 9 1/4" tall, marked Pat. Des. No. 135889, with the poppy decals.*

Spice Jars

*These **Spice Jars one Allspice and one Clove** marked Pat. Des. No. 135889. Both measure 4 3/4" tall.*

Spice Jars

These **Spice Jars one Nutmeg and one Cinnamon** *are marked Pat. Des. No. 135889. Both measure 4 3/4" tall.*

Spice Jars

*These **Spice Jars one Ginger and one Pepper** marked Pat. Des. No. 135889. Both measure 4 3/4" tall.*

Spice Jars & Cannister

*Pictured here is a **Salt Cannister** that measures 9 1/4" tall with a **Pepper and Nutmeg Spice Jar,** each measuring 4 3/4" tall.*

Spice Jar & Salt & Pepper

This very rare **Spice Jar** with blue trim and gold decoration is very hard to find, it measures 4 7/8" tall. The matching **Salt and Pepper** is the small size 3" tall, and they have blue trim.

Standing Bank

These two various versions of the **Standing Bank** are 6 3/4" tall. The blank version is considered very rare. The poppy decorated version is the same size as the blank bank.

Wall Hanging Bank

This **Wall Hanging Bank** is a really great addition to any collection. It usually has the coin slot on the basket as shown. (We have heard from various collectors that these banks have been found with a coin slot on the head). This piece measures 9″ high and is marked Pat. Des. No. 135889 and is considered very rare.

Standing Planter

*This very rare **Standing Planter** measurers 6 3/4" tall and is a real find. Most collectors have never heard of this pieces because it is so rare. The piece is marked Pat. Des. No. 135889.*

Wall Hanging Planter Set

This **Wall Hanging Planter with matching Salt and Peppers and a Butter Dish** all have the unusual "sprig" pattern floral decoration, a very nice collection to have.

Teapots

These **Teapots** show the two different variations of the poppy design decals that were available in the Little Red Riding Hood Line.

Children's Dishes

*These **Children's Dishes** include a serving dish, fork, spoon, and cup.*

Mug

*This is three different views of the **Chocolate Mug** shown here, and the mug is considered very rare.*

Salt and Peppers

These **Salt and Pepper Shakers** depict the different sizes and styles available in the Red Riding Hood line.

Left to Right:
  1st Set - *Kneeling Salt and Pepper Set, unmarked, 5 1/4" tall. These are the Rarest of the sets. This same kneeling salt has appeared as a figurine, without the shaker holes.*
  2nd Set - *These are the Large Size Salt and Pepper Set measuring 5 1/8" tall.*
  3rd Set - *These are the Medium Size Salt and Pepper Set measuring 4 1/2" tall.*
  4th Set - *These are the Small Size Salt and Pepper Set measuring 3" tall.*

Salt and Peppers

*These **Salt and Pepper Shaker Sets** are all the smaller size, 3" tall. Note the different decals and paint, these are a wonderful addition to any collection.*

Lamp

This **Little Red Riding Hood Lamp** is unmarked, but is a very nice piece to add to any collection.

Match Boxes

*These **Wooden Match Holders** both measure 6″ tall. Note the difference in the design and color.*

Match Box

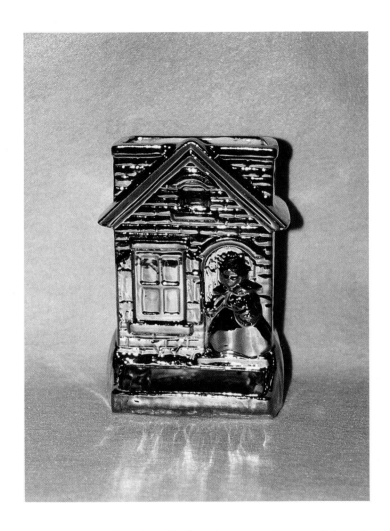

*This **Match Box** is done in gold, these boxes may be mounted on the wall.*

Mustard Jar

*This **Mustard Jar with Spoon** measures 5 1/2" tall and is unmarked.*

Wall Hanging Bank & Stringholder

The **Wall Hanging Bank** *measures 9" tall with the slot in the basket.*

The **Wall Hanging Stringholder** *is 9" tall with the string coming out of the top of the basket. The stringholder is one of the most beautiful and sought after pieces of all.*

Covered Casserole

The **Covered Casserole** that measures 6" tall with the lid, the length of the base is 8 1/4" and with the handle its 4". Marked Pat. Des. No. 135889.

Note the "Bow" design on the base as compared to the 11 3/4" casserole dish on page 43.

PRICE GUIDE

Page 13 - **$425**

Page 14 - **$7,500**

Page 15 - **$1,025**

Page 16 - **$850 each**

Page 18 - **Advertising Plaque $15,000-20,000**

        Baby Dish $8,000

        Covered Casserole $10,000-15,000

        Mug $2,500

        Stringholder $2,500-3,500

        Wall Bank $2,300-2,500

Page 19 - **$1,200 set**

Page 20 - **$575**

Page 21 - **$625-675**

Page 22 - **$650-675**

Page 23 - **$495**

Page 24 - **$495-550**

Page 25 - **$950-1,100**

Page 26 - **$1,500-1,800**

Page 28 - **$1,800**

Page 29 - **Left Jar $575-600**

        Right Jar $900-950

Page 30 - **$850-950**

Page 31 - **$1,400-1,500**

Page 33 - **Left $1,000-1,400**

        Middle $700

        Right $1,250-1,500

PRICE GUIDE

Page 34 - **Left $700**

              Middle $900

              Right $1,400-1,800

Page 35 - **Left $800-1,000**

              Middle $3,000-3,500

              Right $1,500-1,800

Page 36 - **$375 each**

Page 37 - **Covered Sugar $590-650**

              Ruffled Skirt Creamer $575-600

Page 38 - **Open Sugar $225**

              Salt and Pepper $195

              Open Creamer $225

              Cookie Jar $525

Page 39 - **Baby Dish $8,000**

              Mug $2,500

Page 40 - **$500**

Page 41 - **$400**

Page 42 - **Ruffled Skirt Milk Pitcher RARE, the price can not be determined.**

              Pour Through the Head Creamer $575-600

Page 43 - **$10,000-15,000**

Page 44 - **$6,000-7,000**

Page 45 - **Cookies $7,000-8,500**

              Popcorn $7,000-8,000

Page 46 - **$750**

Page 47 - **$750**

Page 48 - **Peanuts $6,000-6,500**

              Potato Chips $6,000-6,500

PRICE GUIDE

Page 49 - **$6,000-7,500**

Page 50 - **$850-900**

Page 51 - **$1,250-1,450**

Page 52 - **$850-900**

Page 53 - **$2,250-2,500**

Page 54 - **$900 each**

Page 55 - **$900 each**

Page 56 - **$900 each**

Page 57 - **Pepper & Nutmeg $900 each**
        Salt $2,250-2,500

Page 58 - **Spice Jar Set $750**

Page 59 - **Blank Bank $1,200**
        Bank with decals $850

Page 60 - **$2,000**

Page 61 - **$20,000**

Page 62 - **Butter Dish $500-550**
        Salt and Pepper $225 set
        Wall Hanging Planter $650-700

Page 63 - **$425**

Page 64 - **Serving Dish $8,000**
        Mug $2,500

Page 65 - **$2,500**

Page 66 - **Kneeling Salt & Pepper $2,000-2,500**
        Large Salt & Pepper $225
        Medium Salt & Pepper $1,250
        Small Salt & Pepper $125-150

PRICE GUIDE

Page 67 - **Left to Right**

   $100

   $450

   $500

   $450

   $100

Page 68 - **$2,500**

Page 69 - **Plain Dress $850-1,200**

   Blue Dress $1,400-1,600

Page 70 - **$1,400**

Page 71 - **$475 w/spoon**

Page 72 - **Wall Hanging Bank $2,300-2,500**

   Wall Hanging Stringholder $2,500-3,500

Page 73 - **$20,000**

another book written
by Mark and Ellen Supnick

COLLECTING
Shawnee Pottery

Shawnee has been a long time favorite of Mark and Ellen's starting with a cookie jar once owned by Mark's mother. This cookie jar sat in her kitchen for many many years, and was admired by everyone when they visited.

With over 800 different pieces, this price guide is packed full of information on the Shawnee Pottery and its distinctive markings. An original Shawnee Company Introduction Letter to the Trade is included in this book, the one the Company issued on September 1937.

The patents are discussed along with the history of the Shawnee Company. This book is very informative and would be a nice book to add to your collection.

Published by **L-W Book Sales, PO Box 69, Gas City, IN 46933**

You may purchase this book from the Authors or the Publisher (their address is on the 2nd page of this book) for **$10.95 + $3.00 shipping.** The book is 76 pages long and is 5 1/2" x 8 1/2", with revised prices.

another book written
by Mark and Ellen Supnick

THE WONDERFUL WORLD OF
COOKIE JARS
A PICTORIAL REFERENCE
AND PRICE GUIDE

The largest single book on cookie jars to be published yet! The Supnick's are the foremost dealers and collectors in the country.

This book includes many different pottery companies such as Redwing Stoneware, Regal China, Shawnee, Brush, Metlox, Twin Winton, Abingdon, American Bisque, Department 56, DeForest of California, Various Walt Disney, Black Americana, Brayton Laguna, and many other Artists are included, to many to mention.

This book would be great to add to your collection.

Published by **L-W Book Sales, PO Box 69, Gas City, IN 46933**

You may purchase this book from the Authors or the Publisher (their address is on the 2nd page of this book) for **$34.95 + $3.00 shipping.** The book is 450 pages long and is 8 1/2" x 11", hardback, revised prices.